(b)

_____

_____

_____

_____

Activity 6
Build a
sentence

minute _____

_____

_____

_____

Activity 7
Edit

Find 6 errors.

thank you! said Luke to Fran

he stooped to stroke Duke

3

Power words
minute
freedom

(a) **Write notes about what dogs need.**

b Write sentences about what dogs need.

The lion's paw

Green words

found   strange   place   floor   saw

Red words

many   one   were   other   through

Your words

(a)

Check

capital letter   Y   comma   ,

full stop   .   speech marks   " "

b

_____

_____

_____

Activity 6
Build a
sentence

horror/horrified   _____

_____

_____

Activity 7
Edit

Find 6 errors.

he sor a cave, dug out of the
hillside. this looks like a good
place to sleep, he said to
himself

Power words
terror/terrified
horror/horrified
courageous

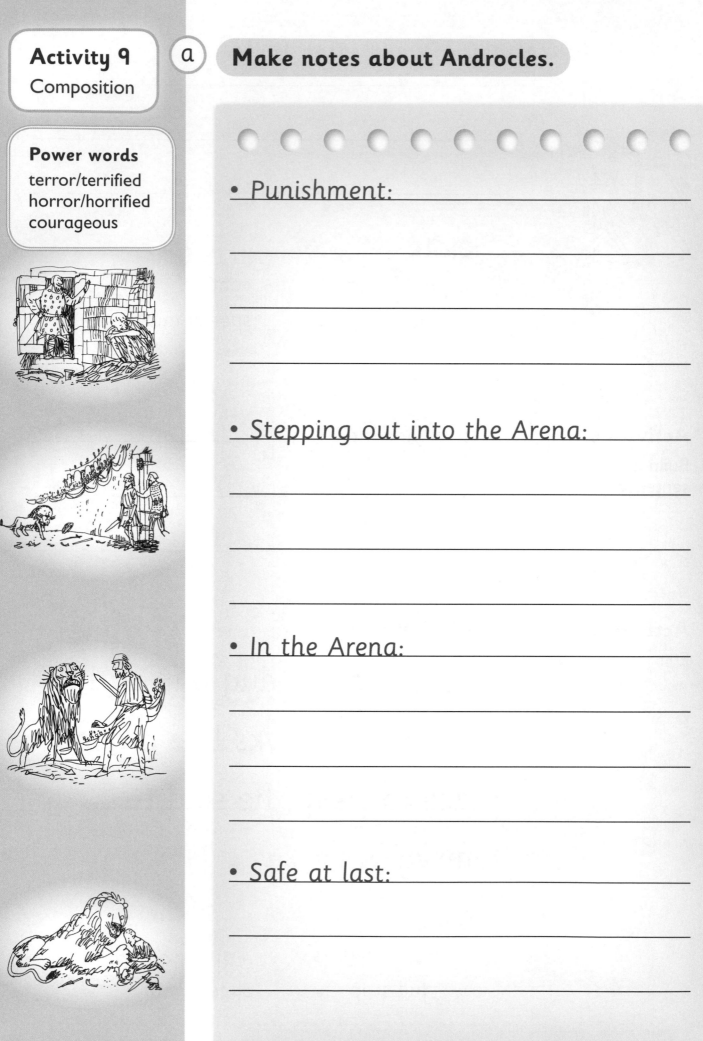

(a) **Make notes about Androcles.**

• Punishment: _____

_____

_____

_____

• Stepping out into the Arena: _____

_____

_____

_____

• In the Arena: _____

_____

_____

_____

• Safe at last: _____

_____

_____

_____

b You are Androcles.
Write about what
happened to you.

I dare you

**Activities
1, 2, 3, 4**
Spelling

Green words

face   stair   hair   care   share

Red words

two   there   who   were   your

Your words

Activity 5
Hold a
sentence

(a)

_____

_____

_____

_____

_____

Check

capital letters W + R + C   question mark ?
apostrophe   '

b

_____

_____

_____

Check

capital letters W + C   question mark   ?

apostrophe   '

Activity 6
Build a
sentence

crammed _____

_____

_____

_____

Activity 7
Edit

Find 6 errors.

i dar you to put on three pars
of moonboots and climb the
mast, said Clare

Check

1 capital letter   2 spell ✗

full stop .   speech marks " "

Power words
cramped
crammed
squeezed

Have you ever played Hide and Seek or Sardines? How did you feel?

Looking after a hamster

Green words

f͟irst   li͡ke   c͡a͡ge   g͟irl   h͟ur͟t

Red words

m⊙th͟er   ⊙th͟er   (are)   w(a)nt   y(our)

Your words

ⓐ

_____

_____

_____

_____

_____

Check

capital letter W   question mark ?

(b)

_____

_____

_____

Activity 6
Build a
sentence

clamber _____

_____

_____

_____

_____

Activity 7
Edit

Find 6 errors.

never let an anmal suffu take
it to the vet if it is ill, so that
he or she can make it better

14

Finish the poem about the hamster that escaped.

Power words
scuttle
scurry
clamber
entice

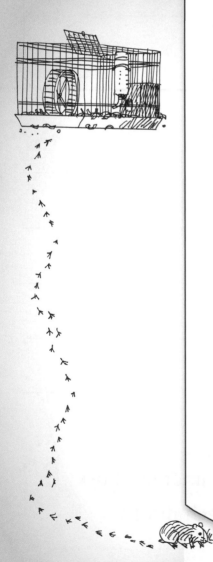

Escaped

We didn't lock the door
We forgot to shut it tight
We should have all made sure
But our pet escaped last night!

_____

_____

_____

_____

_____

_____

_____

_____

_____

_____

How silly!

**Activities
1, 2, 3, 4**
Spelling

Green words

s<u>ou</u>nd r<u>ou</u>nd br<u>ow</u>n t<u>ow</u>n n<u>ow</u>

Red words

h(ere) (wh)(o) th(ere) w(a)ter s(o)n

Your words

Activity 5
Hold a
sentence

(a)

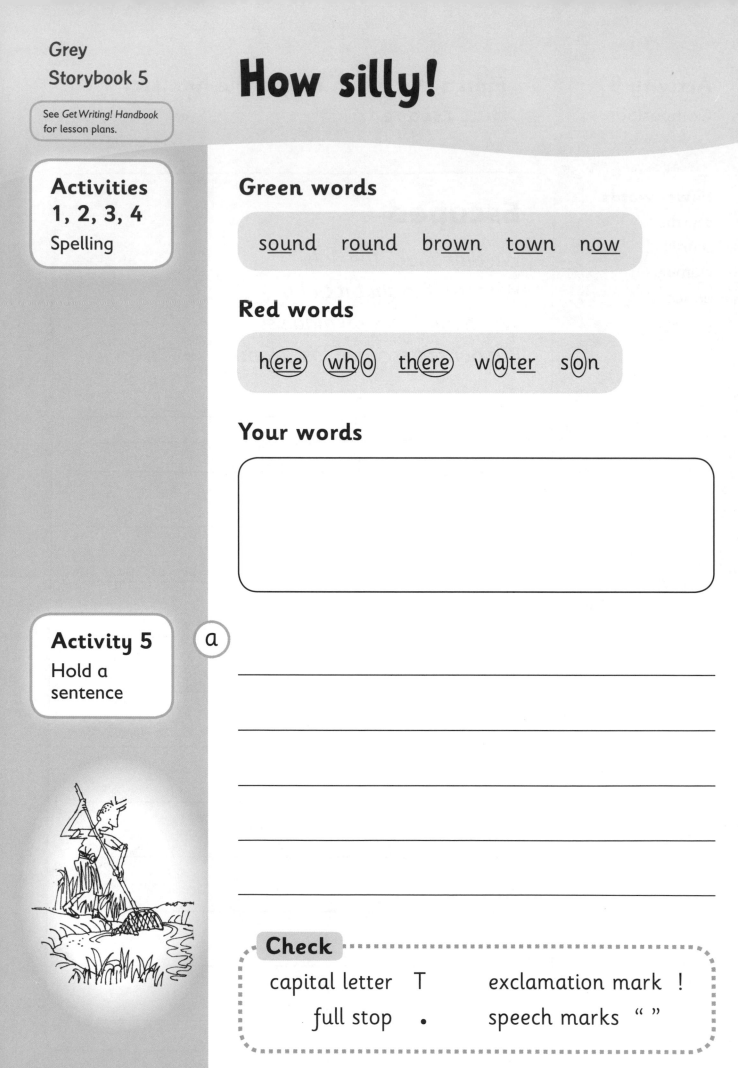

Check

capital letter T   exclamation mark !
full stop .   speech marks " "

16

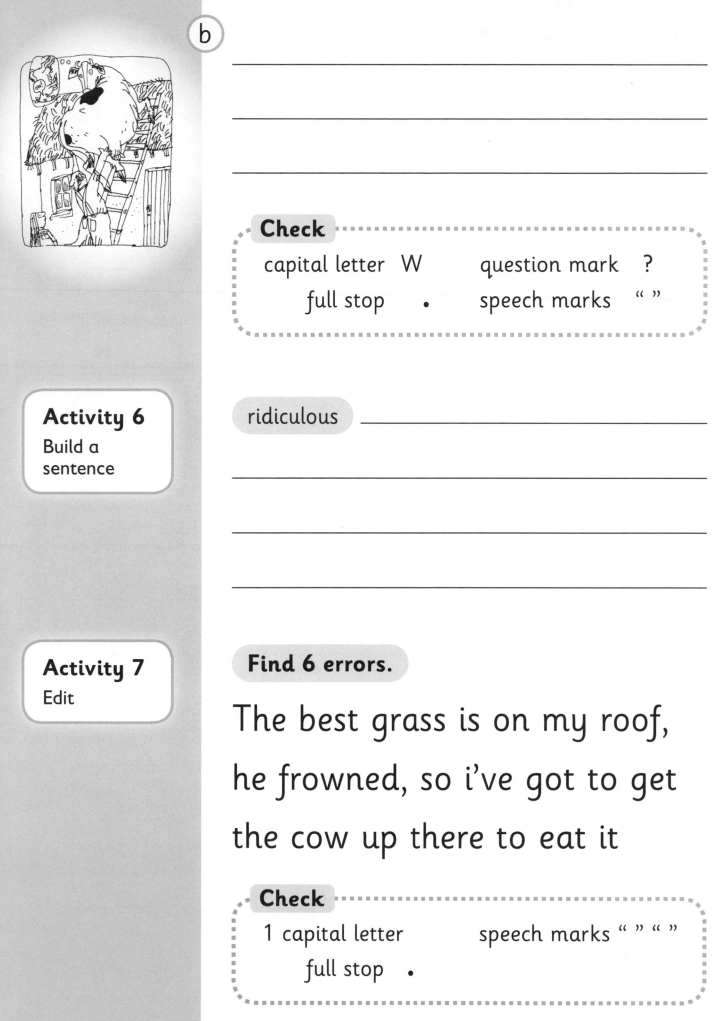

b

_____

_____

_____

Activity 6
Build a sentence

ridiculous _____

_____

_____

_____

Activity 7
Edit

Find 6 errors.

The best grass is on my roof, he frowned, so i've got to get the cow up there to eat it

Activity 9
Composition

(a) **Make notes about when you were embarrassed.**

Power words
ridiculous   nonsense   sensible

b **Now write about what happened.**

When I was embarrassed

_____

_____

_____

_____

_____

_____

_____

_____

_____

The most embarrassing moment was

_____

_____

_____

_____

Wailing Winny's car boot sale

**Activities
1, 2, 3, 4**
Spelling

Green words

take   face   paid   paint   faint

Red words

buy   bought   do   some

Your words

Activity 5

Hold a
sentence

ⓐ

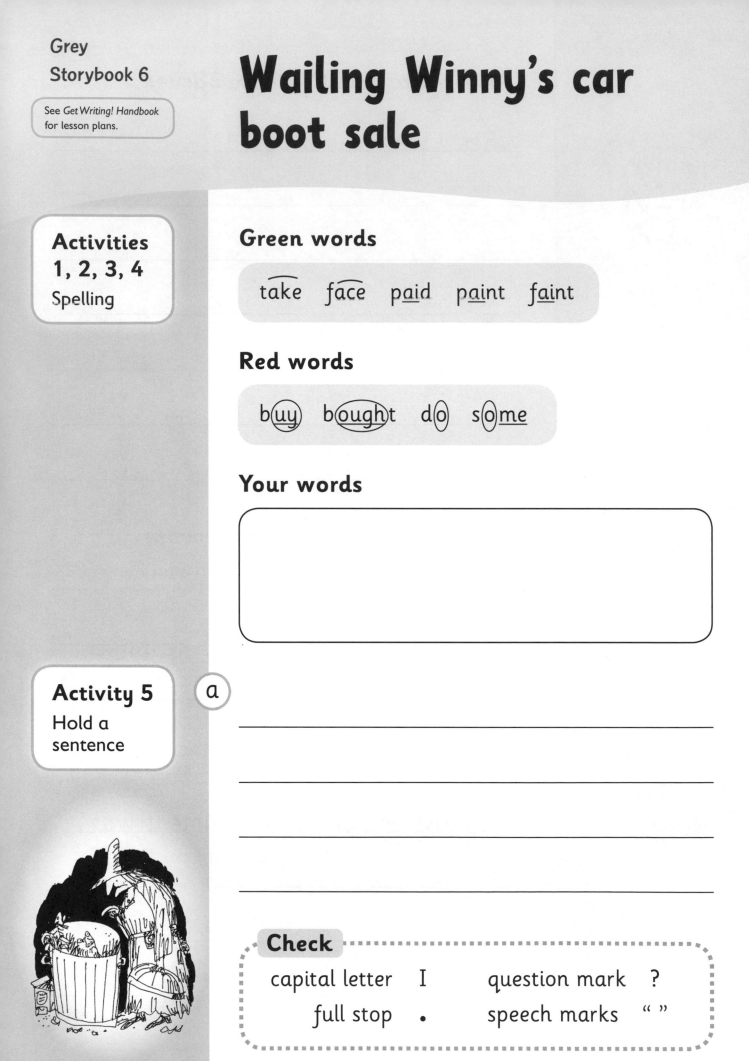

Check

capital letter   I   question mark   ?

full stop   .   speech marks   " "

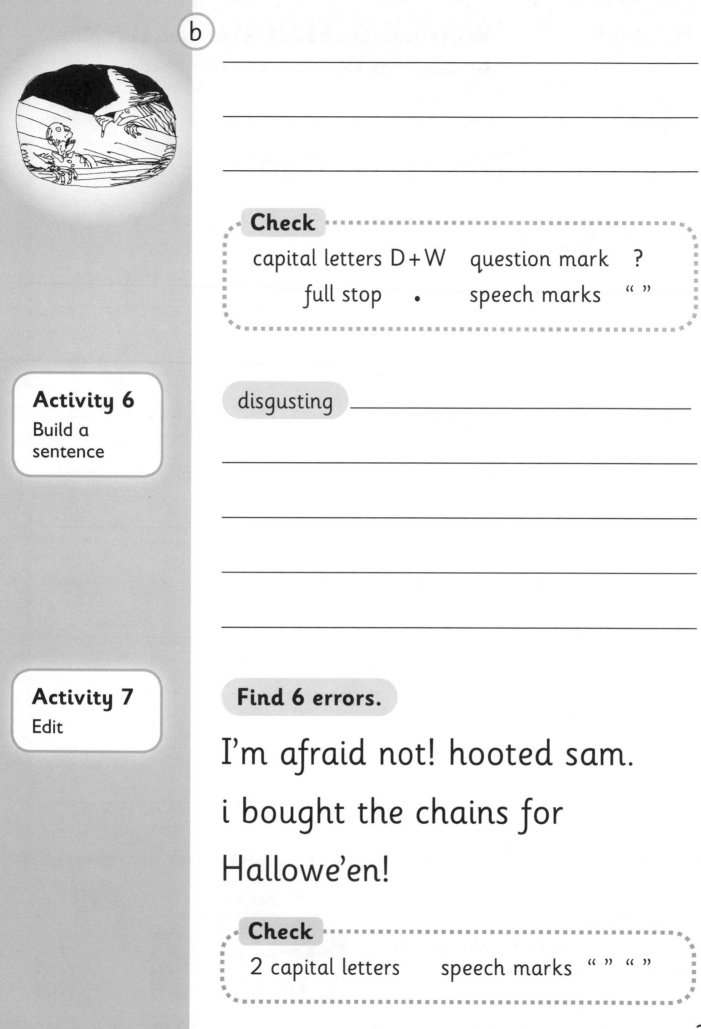

b

_____

_____

_____

Check

capital letters D+W   question mark   ?

full stop   •   speech marks   " "

Activity 6
Build a
sentence

disgusting _____

_____

_____

_____

_____

Activity 7
Edit

Find 6 errors.

I'm afraid not! hooted sam.
i bought the chains for
Hallowe'en!

Check

2 capital letters   speech marks   " " " "

Write a poem about what you can buy at Wailing Winny's car boot sale.

The car boot sale

_____

_____

_____

_____

_____

_____

_____

_____

_____

Power words
useless foul horrible vile mouldy

Toad

**Activities
1, 2, 3, 4**
Spelling

Green words

voi ce   hope   home   throat   coat

Red words

w(ou)(l)d   th(ere)   c(o)me   (a)ny(o)ne   w(a)t(er)

Your words

Activity 5
Hold a
sentence

(a)

_____

_____

_____

_____

_____

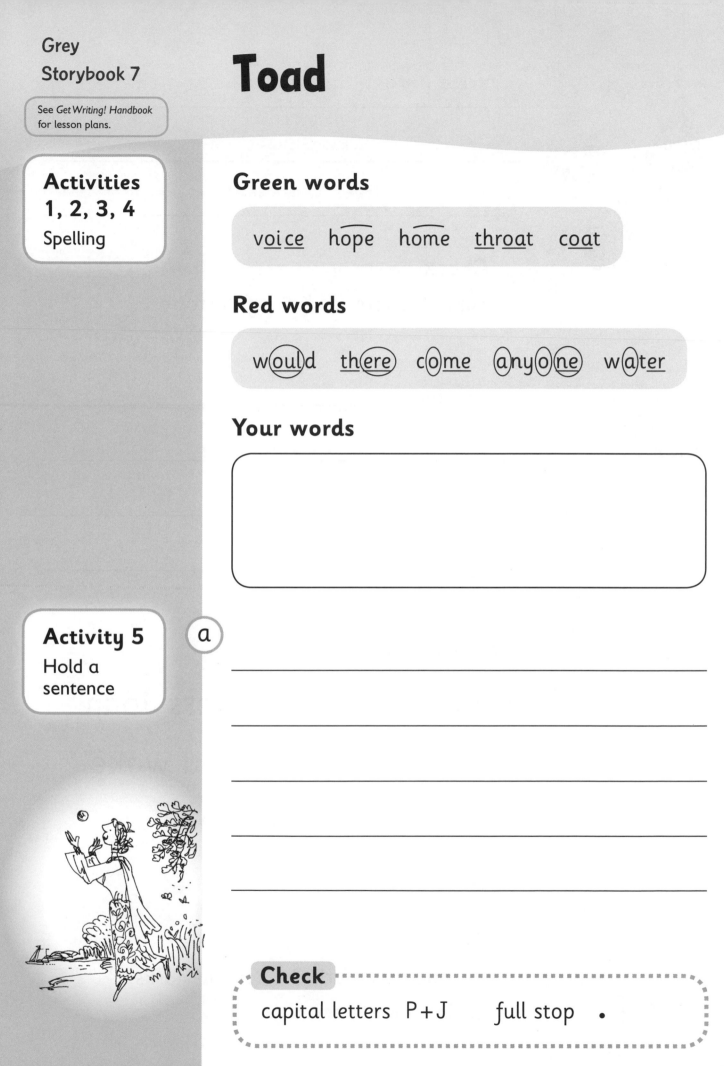

Check
capital letters P+J   full stop .

(b)

_____

_____

_____

Check

capital letters T + K   full stop .

Activity 6
Build a
sentence

deceitful _____

_____

_____

_____

Activity 7
Edit

Find 6 errors.

What's wrong, Princess Joan
croaked the toad. You woke
me up, with your moaning
and groaning

Check

question mark ?   speech marks " " " "
exclamation mark !

24

Write notes about what the characters did and thought.

Write about what lessons the characters learned.

lesson learned

_____

_____

_____

_____

lesson learned

_____

_____

_____

_____

lesson learned

lesson learned

27

Andrew

**Activities
1, 2, 3, 4**
Spelling

Green words

kn ew*   grew   drew   threw   reall`y

Pronounce ew as 'oo'

Red words

wh(ere)   c(ou)ld   wh(a)t   h(ere)   s(o)me (o)ne

Your words

Activity 5
Hold a
sentence

(a)

_____

_____

_____

_____

_____

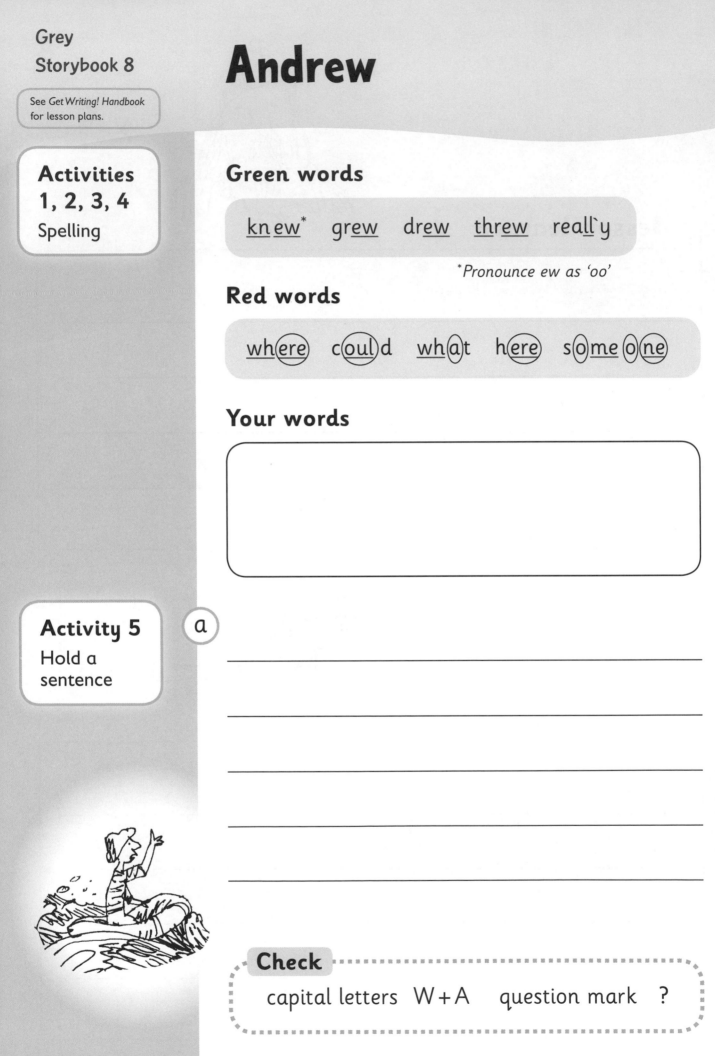

Check

capital letters   W + A   question mark   ?

(b)

_____

_____

_____

Check

capital letter   W   question mark ?

Activity 6
Build a sentence

disappeared   _____

_____

_____

_____

_____

_____

Activity 7
Edit

Find 6 errors.

then someone shouted,

andrew! andrew! can you see

me?

Check

4 capital letters   speech marks   " "

(a)

Make notes about what happened to you when you were lost at sea.

Power words
terrified   horrified   scanned   disappeared

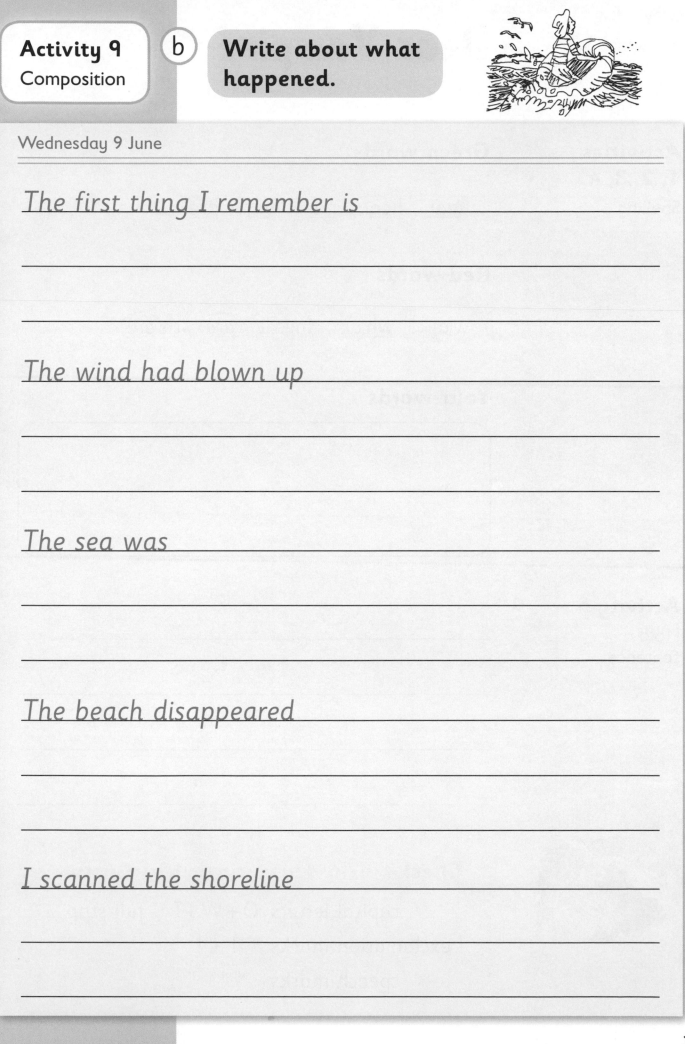

Wednesday 9 June

The first thing I remember is _____

_____

_____

The wind had blown up _____

_____

_____

The sea was _____

_____

_____

The beach disappeared _____

_____

_____

I scanned the shoreline _____

_____

Dear Vampire

Green words

year   hear   ear   fear   fire

Red words

walk   what   small   are   there

Your words

a

Check

capital letters O + W + I   full stop .

exclamation marks   ! + !

speech marks " " " "

32

(b)

_____

_____

_____

Activity 6

Build a sentence

terrifying _____

_____

_____

Activity 7

Edit

Find 6 errors.

sam was dancing with nelly

dave was playing a tune on

his dustbin lids. phil was

lighting the fireworks

Activity 9
Composition

a **Make notes for your writing.**

Power words
terrifying
horrifying
frightening
blood-curdling

Write a letter to the vampire. Give him some good advice about how to be more scary.

Dear Aunt Horrible,

I am sad and confused. I was asked to terrify a group of witches and ghouls but it all went wrong. They said I was the worst vampire ever. I came as a bat, which I thought was pretty frightening but they just thought I was pathetic and really a rather rubbish vampire. Help me, please...

Dear Vampire,

_____

_____

_____

_____

_____

_____

_____

_____

_____

_____

Vulture culture

Green words

huge   white   year   more   be`cause

Red words

their   where   many   were   come

Your words

Activity 5
Hold a
sentence

(a)

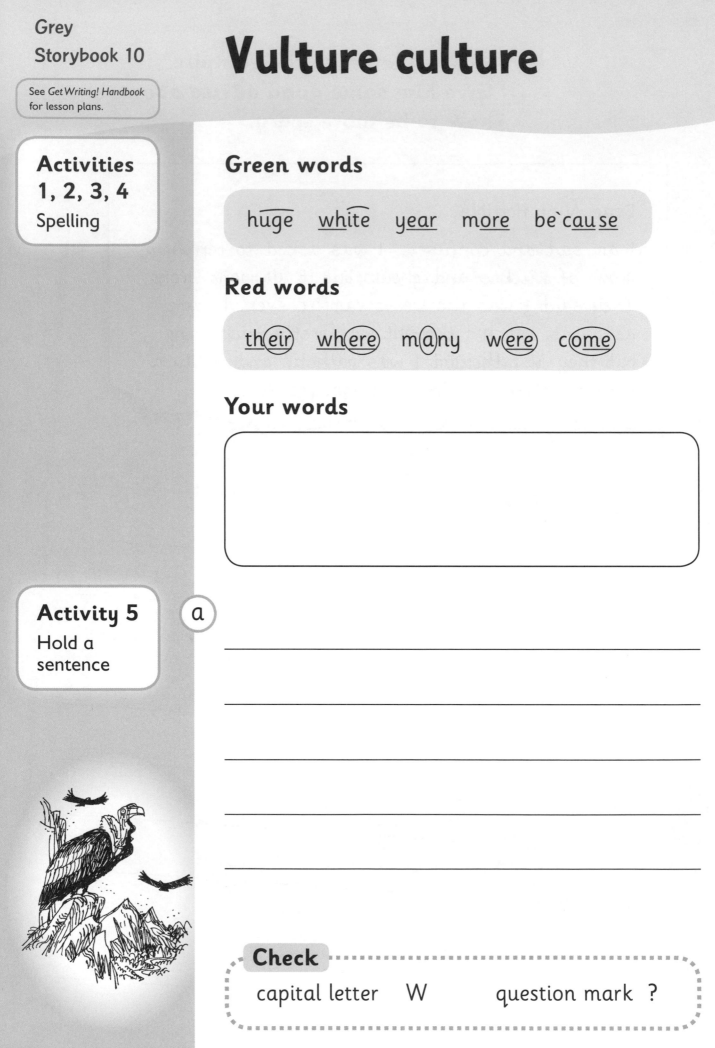

Check

capital letter   W   question mark ?

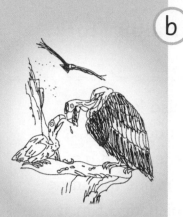

(b)

_____

_____

_____

Activity 6
Build a
sentence

scavenge/scavenger   _____

_____

_____

Activity 7
Edit

Find 6 errors.

there are now many more
condors the future looks good
for these proud creatures we
will have the pleasure of seeing
them for many years to come

Check

3 capital letters   full stops   •••

37

(a) **Write notes about the Marabou stork.**

The Marabou stork from Africa is also known as the 'undertaker bird' because of its huge, black, cloak-like wings. It has skinny white legs and a pink bald head and it stands 150 cm tall. It has the same wingspan as the Andean condor which, at 3.5 m, is the largest of any bird.

Like the Andean condor, the Marabou stork is a scavenger, eating dead animals. It can also capture small animals and birds such as rats and doves. It lays up to 3 eggs at a time and nests on cliff edges or in trees in a colony with other Marabou storks.

- Looks like: _____

_____

- Eats: _____

_____

- Lives: _____

_____

- Breeds: _____

_____

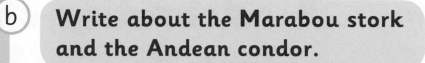

b **Write about the Marabou stork and the Andean condor.**

Similarities and differences between the Marabou stork and the Andean condor

_____

_____

_____

_____

_____

_____

_____

_____

_____

_____

A celebration on planet Zox

Green words

sta`tion   sec`tion   trad`i`tion   explore
invite

Red words

worse   call   said   should   watch

Your words

(a)

_____

_____

_____

_____

Check

capital letters   M + M   full stop   .

(b)

_____

_____

_____

Check

capital letters   W + C   speech marks   " "

full stop   •   apostrophe   '

question mark   ?

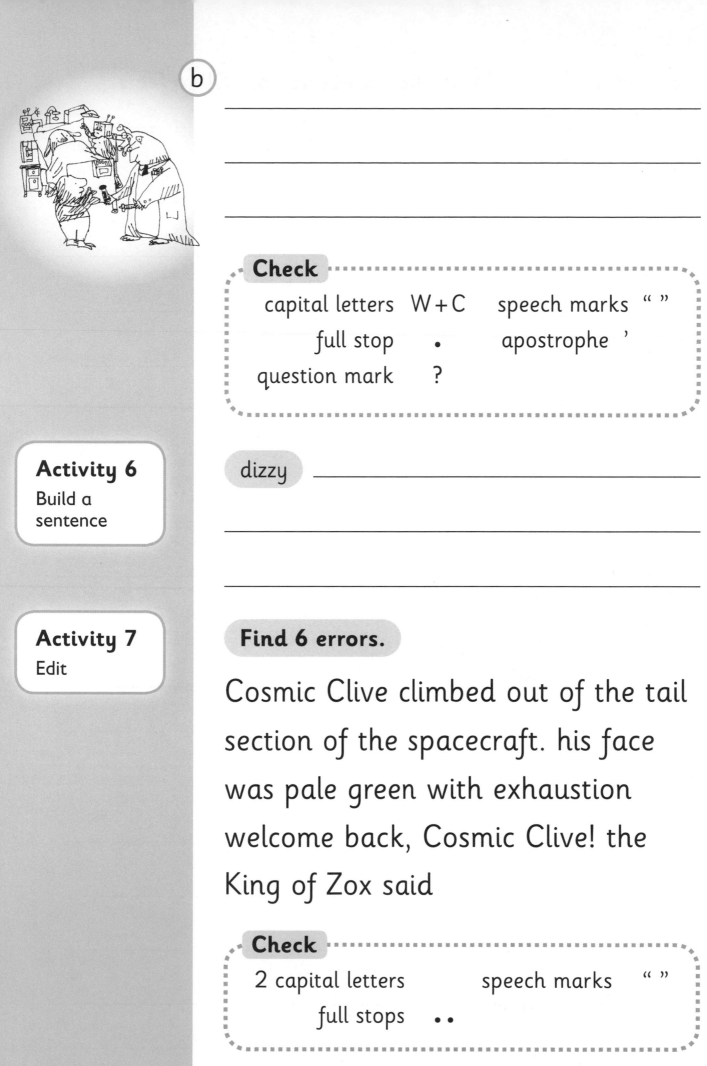

Activity 6
Build a sentence

dizzy _____

_____

_____

Activity 7
Edit

Find 6 errors.

Cosmic Clive climbed out of the tail section of the spacecraft. his face was pale green with exhaustion welcome back, Cosmic Clive! the King of Zox said

Check

2 capital letters   speech marks   " "

full stops   • •

41

Activity 9
Composition

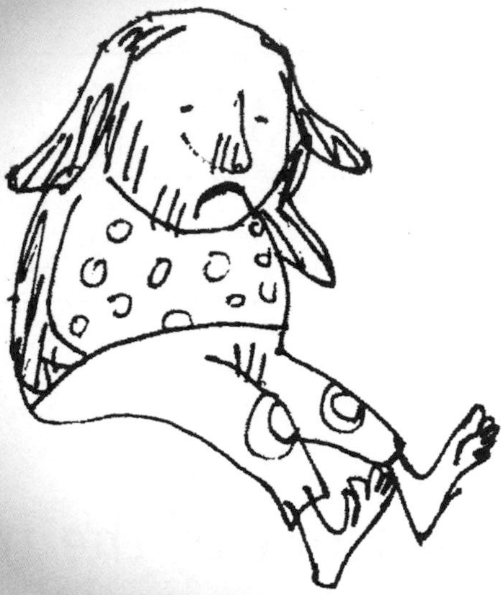

Power words
light-headed
burning up
sweaty
aching all over

a Write notes about how Clive feels.

How did you feel
before you fell over?

_____

_____

_____

Can I look at your
tummy? What do the
spots feel like, and when
did they appear?

_____

_____

_____

A very dangerous dinosaur

**Activities
1, 2, 3, 4**
Spelling

Green words

se`ri`<u>ous</u>   cu`ri`<u>ous</u>   de`li`<u>ci</u>ous   fe`ro`<u>ci</u>ous
pre`<u>ci</u>ous

Red words

th<u>ough</u>t   th(ere)   wh(ere)   thr(ough)   w(oul)d

Your words

Activity 5
Hold a
sentence

(a)

> Scrumptious!

Check

capital letters H+S   exclamation mark !
full stops   ..   speech marks " "

(b)

_____

_____

_____

ferocious _____

_____

_____

Find 6 errors.

When she returned the two egs had gone she saw Snatchosaurus disappearing behind a rock, spitting out bits of shell "oh no," she wailed

Power words
ferocious
devious
dangerous
deadly

(a) **Design and describe your dinosaur.**

_____

_____

_____

_____

_____

(b) **Write a poem about Catchasnatchosaurus.**

_____

_____

_____

_____

_____

_____

_____

47

The invisible clothes

**Activities
1, 2, 3, 4**

Spelling

*Note: do not
use Fred fingers
to spell these
words.
Note: most 'ible'
words do not
have a root.*

Green words

ho`rri`ble   po`ssi`ble   te`rri`ble   in`cre`di`ble
in`vi`si`ble

Red words

bought   thought   through   father
any

Your words

Activity 5

Hold a
sentence

a

Check

capital letter   I   full stop   .

speech marks   " "   apostrophe   '

exclamation mark   !

(b)

_____

_____

_____

Activity 6
Build a
sentence

humiliated _____

_____

_____

Activity 7
Edit

Find 6 errors.

a small boy was in the crowd
with his father the Emperor
isn't wearing any clothes! he
whispered

Activity 9
Composition

(a) **Make notes about the Emperor before and after he is tricked.**

Power words
proud
humiliated
embarrassed

Before

- <u>Feels:</u> _____
- _____
- _____
- _____

- <u>Moves:</u> _____
- _____
- _____
- _____

- <u>Thinks:</u> _____
- _____
- _____
- _____

After

- <u>Feels:</u> _____

- _____

- _____

- _____

- <u>Moves:</u> _____

- _____

- _____

- _____

- <u>Thinks:</u> _____

- _____

- _____

- _____

b Write a letter to a friend about the trick.

A job for Jordan

**Activities
1, 2, 3, 4**
Spelling

Green words

for   more   paw   morn`ing   be`fore

Red words

all   come   they   who   you

Your words

Activity 5
Hold a
sentence

ⓐ

Check

capital letter   H   full stop   .

(b)

_____

_____

_____

Check

capital letter   D   question mark ?

Activity 6
Build a
sentence

persuade _____

_____

_____

_____

_____

Activity 7
Edit

Find 6 errors.

all pups can be plyful, but a
guide dog pup has to behave his
owner's lif will be in his hands

Check

2 capital letters   2 spell ✗
     full stops   . .

Design a poster to raise money to train a guide dog.

Power words
support   important

A place in space: the Moon

**Activities
1, 2, 3, 4**
Spelling

Green words

place   take   same   shape   life

Red words

any   does   there   what   who

Your words

Activity 5
Hold a
sentence

(a)

_____

_____

_____

_____

Check
capital letters T + M   full stop   .

(b)

_____

_____

_____

Activity 6
Build a sentence

gravity _____

_____

_____

_____

_____

Activity 7
Edit

Find 6 errors.

there is no air on the Moon if
you go to the Moon you must
tak air wiv you in tanks

57

(a) **Plan your poem about walking on the Moon.**

b Write your poem about walking on the Moon.

Complex Speed Sounds

Consonant sounds

f ff ph	l ll le	m mm mb	n nn kn	r rr wr	s ss se c ce	v ve	z zz s se	sh ti ci	th	ng nk

b bb	c k ck ch	d dd	g gg	h	j g ge dge	p pp	qu	t tt	w wh	x	y	ch tch

Vowel sounds

a	e ea	i	o	u	ay a-e ai	ee y ea e	igh i-e ie i y	ow o-e oa o

oo u-e ue ew	oo	ar	or oor ore aw au	air are	ir ur er	ou ow	oy oi	ire	ear	ure

Red words to spell

I the said does do

me he be she why

no go so put what

was were want of you

your my to are her

all small buy by

some they one

there their here should

OXFORD
UNIVERSITY PRESS

Great Clarendon Street, Oxford OX2 6DP

Oxford University Press is a department of the University of Oxford.
It furthers the University's objective of excellence in research, scholarship,
and education by publishing worldwide in

Oxford New York

Auckland Cape Town Dar es Salaam Hong Kong Karachi
Kuala Lumpur Madrid Melbourne Mexico City Nairobi
New Delhi Shanghai Taipei Toronto

With offices in

Argentina Austria Brazil Chile Czech Republic France Greece
Guatemala Hungary Italy Japan Poland Portugal Singapore
South Korea Switzerland Thailand Turkey Ukraine Vietnam

Oxford is a registered trade mark of Oxford University Press
in the UK and in certain other countries

British Library Cataloguing in Publication Data

Data available

ISBN: 978-0-19-847909-3

10 9 8 7 6 5 4 3 2 1

Printed in China by Hing Yip

Acknowledgements

The publisher would like to thank the following for permission to reproduce
photographs: **P39a-b** rusm/iStock.com; **P53** Altrendo Images/Getty; **P54** Yuri Arcurs/
Shutterstock.com; **P55** Kevin Wheatley/Shutterstock.com; **P56** Manfred Konrad/
iStock.com; **P57** Media Union/Shutterstock.com; **P59** Triff/Shutterstock.com

Illustrations by Tim Archbold and Rosie Brooks

Design by PDQ

Paper used in the production of this book is a natural, recyclable product
made from wood grown in sustainable forests. The manufacturing process
conforms to the environmental regulations of the country of origin.

Written by Charlotte Raby and Ruth Miskin

Hold a sentence texts

Storybook 1: Rex to the rescue

a) What was the big problem between the dogs?

b) "Sploosh!" barked Duke, with his mouth full of green slime.

Storybook 2: The lion's paw

a) "You have broken the law," he said.

b) "You must be punished," he shouted.

Storybook 3: I dare you

a) What is Rob's first dare to Clare?

b) Why does he think Clare's dare is not fair?

Storybook 4: Looking after a hamster

a) What do you need to buy for your hamster?

b) What can you make hamster toys from?

Storybook 5: How silly!

a) "The sun has fallen into the pond!" he shouted.

b) "Why have you done such a silly thing?" she asked.

Storybook 6: Wailing Winny's car boot sale

a) "Is it dustbin day?" he grunted.

b) "Did you buy a pair of trainers at the sale?" wailed Winnie.

Storybook 7: Toad

a) Princess Joan lived in a palace by a lake.

b) The King often boasted about her good looks.

Storybook 8: Andrew

a) Why was Andrew really scared?

b) What if he floated here forever?

Storybook 9: Dear Vampire

a) "Oh dear!" wailed Winnie. "I wanted a scary vampire!"

b) "I'm getting tired of this!" wailed Winny.

Storybook 10: Vulture culture

a) Why do you think condors should be protected?

b) Why do they stay with their parents for so long?

Storybook 11: A celebration on planet Zox

a) Mum was deep in conversation with Meg.

b) "Will he need an operation?" asked Clare's mum.

Storybook 12: A very dangerous dinosaur

a) He wiped his hideous mouth. "Scrumptious!" he cried.

b) "It is a very dangerous dinosaur," he said.

Storybook 13: The invisible clothes

a) "I can't see the cloth!" he cried miserably.

b) Isn't this the most remarkable fabric you have ever seen?

Non-fiction Book 1: A job for Jordan

a) He is trained in some more important lessons.

b) Do you want to sponsor a guide dog pup?

Non-fiction Book 5: A place in space: the Moon

a) The Moon is the same shape as a ball.

b) Is the Moon high up in space?

Read Write Inc. PHONICS
Get Writing!

Get Writing! Grey Book 7

The **Get Writing! Books** contain a wide range of writing activities which are linked to the Storybooks and Non-fiction Books to make the strong link between reading and writing. Lesson plans for the writing activities are provided in the **Get Writing! Handbook**.

The writing activities and features include:

- Remembering and writing a sentence

- Finding spelling and punctuation errors in a sentence

- Composition activities which develop children's writing step-by-step from simple sentences to extended texts. Children write a variety of texts including: dialogue, recounts, non-chronological reports, instructions, descriptive texts, writing from experience, labels, poems and letters

- 'Check' boxes which prompt children to review their writing throughout

- Focus on 'power words' which encourages children to use ambitious vocabulary in their writing.

Use the **Get Writing! Books** with the Storybooks as follows:

Get Writing! Red Ditty Books 1–10	Red Ditty Books 1–10
Get Writing! Green Book 1	Set 1 Green Storybooks 1–10
Get Writing! Purple Book 2	Set 2 Purple Storybooks 1–10
Get Writing! Pink Book 3	Set 3 Pink Storybooks 1–10
Get Writing! Orange Book 4	Set 4 Orange Storybooks 1–12
Get Writing! Yellow Book 5	Set 5 Yellow Storybooks 1–10
Get Writing! Blue Book 6	Set 6 Blue Storybooks 1–10
Get Writing! Grey Book 7	Set 7 Grey Storybooks 1–13

Not to be phot d

OXFORD
UNIVERSITY PRESS

How to get in touch:
web   www.oxfordprimary.co.uk
email   schools.enquiries.uk@oup.com
tel.   +44 (0) 1536 452610
fax   +44 (0) 1865 313472

ISBN 978-0-19-84

9 780198 479

KS-939-747